BIG BOOK OF MOVIE AND TV THEMES

ISBN 0-7935-1627-7

Hal Leonard Publishing Corporation

7777 West Bluemound Road P.O. Box 13819 Milwaukee, WI 53213

The Big Book Of Movie And TV Themes

* Academy Award Winner

THEME FROM "THE A TEAM"

Words and Music by MIKE POST
and PETE CARPENTER

ALFRED HITCHCOCK PRESENTS

By D. KAHN
and M. LENARD

AMERICA
(From the Motion Picture "THE JAZZ SINGER")

Words and Music by
NEIL DIAMOND

BACK TO THE FUTURE

By ALAN SILVESTRI

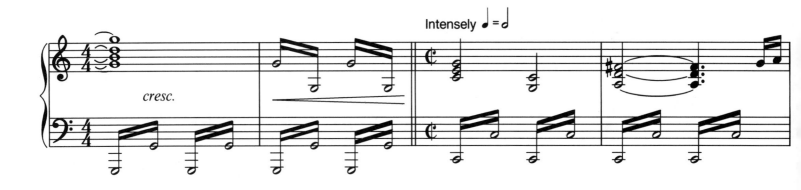

MCA music publishing

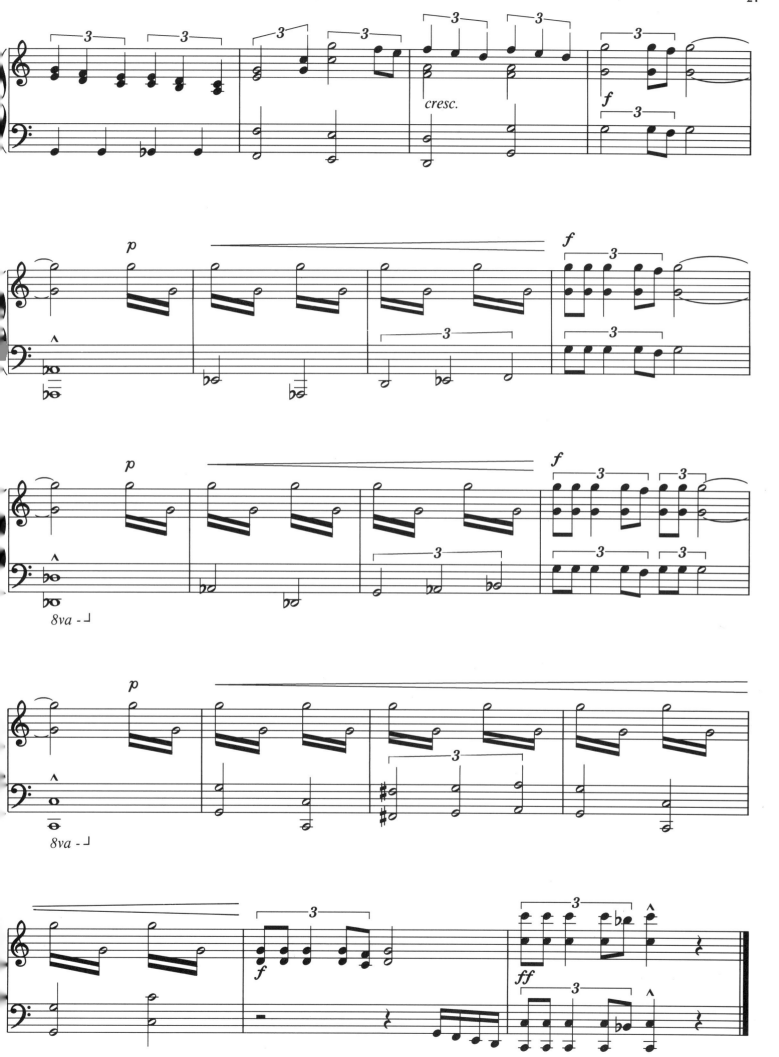

THE BALLAD OF DAVY CROCKETT
(From "Davy Crockett, King Of The Wild Frontier")

Words by TOM BLACKBURN
Music by GEORGE BRUNS

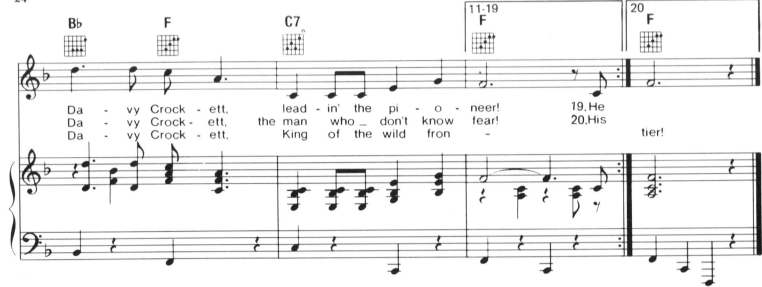

				11-19	20
Bb	F	C7		F	F

Da - vy Crock - ett, lead - in' the pi - o - neer!   19. He
Da - vy Crock - ett, the man who _ don't know fear!   20. His
Da - vy Crock - ett, King of the wild fron - tier!

VERSES

4.
Andy Jackson is our gen'ral's name,
His reg'lar soldiers we'll put to shame,
Them redskin varmints us Volunteers'll tame,
'Cause we got the guns with the sure-fire aim.
Davy — Davy Crockett,
The champion of us all!

5.
Headed back to war from the ol' home place,
But Red Stick was leadin' a merry chase,
Fightin' an' burnin' at a devil's pace
South to the swamps on the Florida Trace.
Davy — Davy Crockett,
Trackin' the redskins down!

6.
Fought single-handed through the Injun War
Till the Creeks was whipped an' peace was in store,
An' while he was handlin' this risky chore,
Made hisself a legend for evermore.
Davy — Davy Crockett,
King of the wild frontier!

7.
He give his word an' he give his hand
That his Injun friends could keep their land,
An' the rest of his life he took the stand
That justice was due every redskin band.
Davy — Davy Crockett,
Holdin' his promise dear!

8.
Home fer the winter with his family,
Happy as squirrels in the ol' gum tree,
Bein' the father he wanted to be,
Close to his boys as the pod an' the pea.
Davy — Davy Crockett,
Holdin' his young 'uns dear!

9.
But the ice went out an' the warm winds came
An' the meltin' snow showed tracks of game,
An' the flowers of Spring filled the woods with flame,
An' all of a sudden life got too tame.
Davy — Davy Crockett,
Headin' on West again!

10.
Off through the woods we're riding' along,
Makin' up yarns an' singin' a song,
He's ringy as a b'ar an' twict as strong,
An' knows he's right 'cause he ain't often wrong.
Davy — Davy Crockett,
The man who don't know fear!

11.
Lookin' fer a place where the air smells clean,
Where the trees is tall an' the grass is green,
Where the fish is fat in an untouched stream,
An' the teemin' woods is a hunter's dream.
Davy — Davy Crockett,
Lookin' fer Paradise!

12.
Now he'd lost his love an' his grief was gall,
In his heart he wanted to leave it all,
An' lose himself in the forests tall,
But he answered instead his country's call.
Davy — Davy Crockett,
Beginnin' his campaign!

13.
Needin' his help they didn't vote blind,
They put in Davy 'cause he was their kind,
Sent up to Nashville the best they could find,
A fightin' spirit an' a thinkin' mind.
Davy — Davy Crockett,
Choice of the whole frontier!

14.
The votes were counted an' he won hands down,
So they sent him off to Washin'ton town
With his best dress suit still his buckskins brown,
A livin' legend of growin' renown.
Davy — Davy Crockett,
The Canebrake Congressman!

15.
He went off to Congress an' served a spell,
Fixin' up the Gover'ment an' laws as well,
Took over Washin'ton so we heered tell
An' patched up the crack in the Liberty Bell.
Davy — Davy Crockett,
Seein' his duty clear!

16.
Him an' his jokes travelled all through the land,
An' his speeches made him friends to beat the band,
His politickin' was their favorite brand
An' everyone wanted to shake his hand.
Davy — Davy Crockett,
Helpin' his legend grow!

17.
He knew when he spoke he sounded the knell
Of his hopes for White House an' fame as well,
But he spoke out strong so hist'ry books tell
An patched up the crack in the Liberty Bell.
Davy — Davy Crockett,
Seein' his duty clear!

BANDSTAND BOOGIE

Words by BARRY MANILOW
and BRUCE SUSSMAN
Music by CHARLES ALBERTINE

The sing - er's

croon - in',   he ain't the great - est, but gee,   my ba - by's swoon - in',   in front of
hop - pin',   and we'll be hop - pin' all day   where things are pop - pin'   the Phil - a -

all of T. V.   So if you tune in,   you'll see my ba - by and me   on the
del - phi - a way. And you can drop in   on all the mu - sic they play   on the

Band - stand, —   Band - stand. — And now we're Band - stand. — And we'll rock and roll and
Band - stand, —

Guitar Tacet

BEAUTY AND THE BEAST

(From Walt Disney's "BEAUTY AND THE BEAST")

Words by HOWARD ASHMAN
Music by ALAN MENKEN

THEME FROM "BEN CASEY"

By DAVID RAKSIN

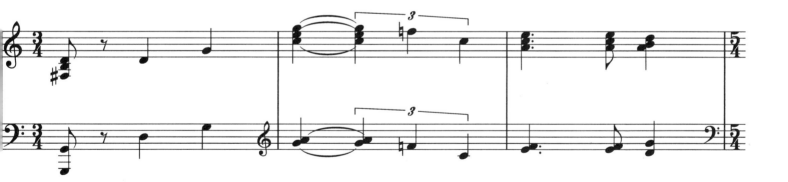

To Coda ⊕

BLAZE OF GLORY
(From the Film "Young Guns II")

Words and Music by
JON BON JOVI

wake up in the morn-ing and I raise my wear-y head,_____ I've got an

night I go to bed, I pray the Lord my soul to keep._ No I ain't

Additional Lyrics (Album version)

2. When you're brought into this world
   They say you're born in sin.
   Well, at least they gave me something
   I didn't have to steal or have to win.
   Well, they tell me that I'm wanted
   Yeah, I'm a wanted man.
   I'm a colt in your stable,
   I'm what Cain was to Abel.
   Mister, catch me if you can.

BONANZA
(Theme From TV Series)

Words and Music by RAY EVANS
and JAY LIVINGSTON

Medium tempo - deliberately, with a heavy beat

We got a right to pick a lit-tle fight, bo-nan - za! _____
This is the night I'm gon-na hit a bright bo-nan - za! _____

If an-y-one fights an-y-one of us
I bet a buck I hit a bit o' luck

he's got-ta fight with me! _____
that's how it's gon-na be. _____

MCA music publishing

CANDLE ON THE WATER

(From Walt Disney Productions "PETE'S DRAGON")

Words and Music by AL KASHA
and JOEL HIRSCHHORN

I'll be your can - dle on the wa - ter,
My love for you will al - ways burn.
I know you're lost and drift - ing,
But the clouds are lift - ing,
don't give up you have some - where to turn.

I'll be your can - dle on the wa - ter,
'Til ev - 'ry wave is warm and bright,
My soul is there be - side you,
Let this can - dle guide you
soon you'll see a gold - en stream of light.

CHIM CHIM CHER-EE
(From Walt Disney's "MARY POPPINS")

Words and Music by RICHARD M. SHERMAN
and ROBERT B. SHERMAN

THEME FROM "COACH"

By JOHN MORRIS

MCA music publishing

8va bassa - - - - - - - - - - - - - - -

CHAMPAGNE TIME

Words and Music by
GEORGE CATES

DREAMS TO DREAM

(From the Universal Motion Picture "AN AMERICAN TAIL: FIEVEL GOES WEST")

Words and Music by JAMES HORNER
and WILL JENNINGS

DALLAS
(Theme From The Lorimar Productions, Inc. Television Series)

Music by JERROLD IMMEL

DANNY BOY
(From "THE DANNY THOMAS SHOW")

ENDLESS LOVE

Words and Music by
LIONEL RICHIE

Oh, _____ and _ love. _____

I'll be that fool for _____ you _____ I'm _____ sure;_

you _ know I don't mind. _____ And yes, _____

THEME FROM E.T.
(THE EXTRA-TERRESTRIAL)

Music by JOHN WILLIAMS

Piano Solo

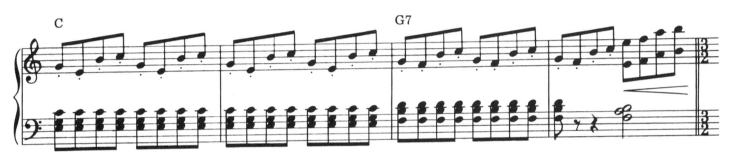

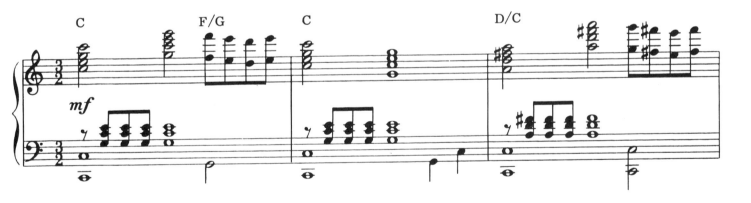

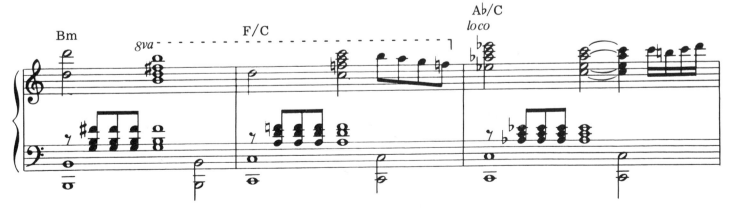

THE EXODUS SONG

Words by PAT BOONE
Music by ERNEST GOLD

EVERYBODY'S TALKIN'
(Echoes)

Words and Music by
FRED NEIL

FALCON CREST

(Theme From The Lorimar Productions, Inc. Television Series)

Music by BILL CONTI

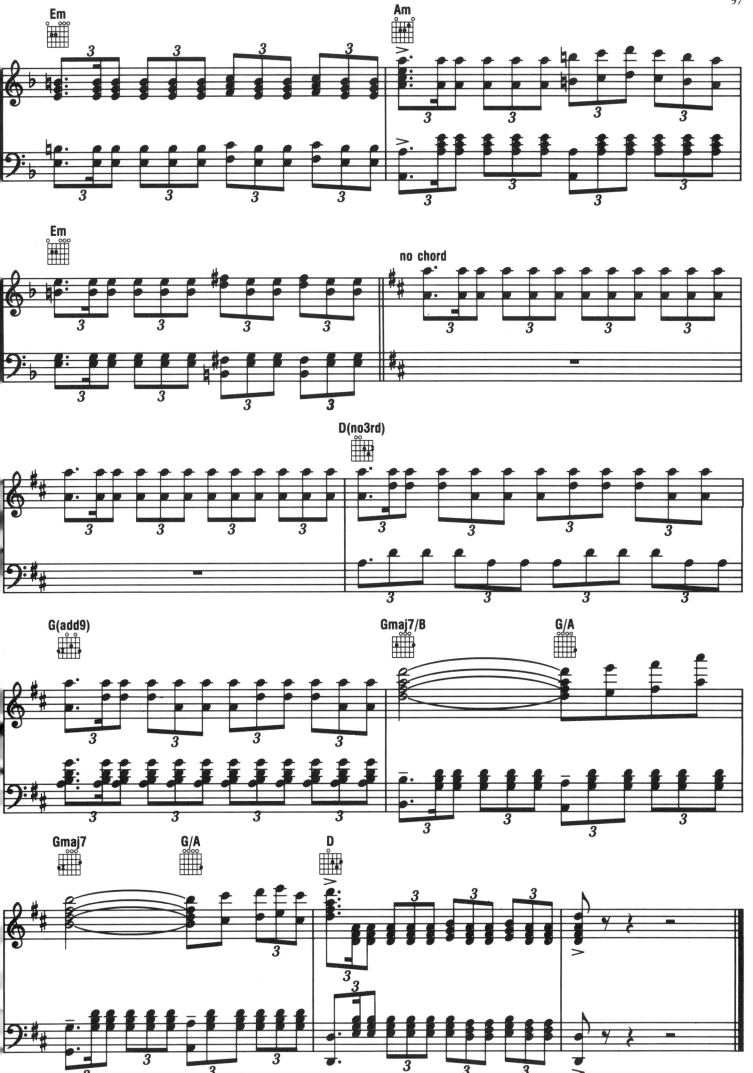

FATHER KNOWS BEST THEME

(From "FATHER KNOWS BEST")

By DON FERRIS
and IRVING FRIEDMAN

FLASHDANCE...WHAT A FEELING

Lyrics by KEITH FORSEY and IRENE CARA
Music by GIORGIO MORODER

FOR ALL WE KNOW
(From The Motion Picture "LOVERS AND OTHER STRANGERS")

Words by ROBB WILSON and JAMES GRIFFIN
Music by FRED KARLIN

(MEET) THE FLINTSTONES

(From "THE FLINTSTONES")

Words and Music by W. HANNA,
J. BARBERA and H. CURTIN

GEORGY GIRL

Words by JIM DALE
Music by TOM SPRINGFIELD

GET SMART

Words and Music by
IRVING SZATHMARY

GIGI
(From "GIGI")

Words by ALAN JAY LERNER
Music by FREDERICK LOEWE

THEME FROM "THE GREATEST AMERICAN HERO"

Words by STEPHEN GEYER
Music by MIKE POST

125

GILLETTE LOOK SHARP MARCH

By MAHLON MERRICK

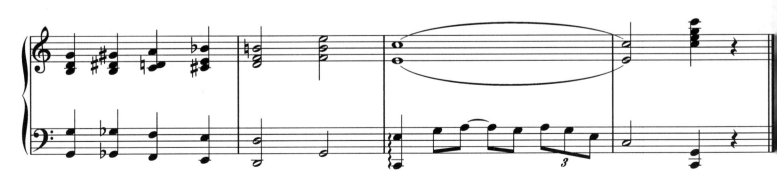

A HARD DAY'S NIGHT

Words and Music by JOHN LENNON
and PAUL McCARTNEY

MCA music publishing

HAWAII FIVE-O

Words and Music by
MORT STEVENS

With a driving beat

HAWAIIAN EYE

By MACK DAVID
and JERRY LIVINGSTON

HBO MAIN THEME

© 1982, 1986 L-T Music

By FERDINAND JAY SMITH III

D.S. al Coda

CODA

HOGAN'S HEROES MARCH

By JERRY FIELDING

HOW DEEP IS YOUR LOVE

(From The Motion Picture "SATURDAY NIGHT FEVER")

Words and Music by BARRY GIBB,
MAURICE GIBB and ROBIN GIBB

Moderately

I know your eyes in the morn - ing sun.____
I be - lieve in you.____ I feel you touch
You know the door.

____ me in the pour - ing rain.____ And the mo - ment that you wan - der far____
to my ver - y soul.____ You're the light ____ in my deep - est, dark

Is Your Love? I real-ly mean to learn. 'Cause we're liv-ing in a world of fools, break-ing us down when they all should let us be. We be long to you and me.

D.S. and Fade

How Deep

HUSH HUSH, SWEET CHARLOTTE

Words and Music by MACK DAVID
and FRANK DeVOL

Slowly and sweetly

Hush, hush, sweet Char - lotte,

Char-lotte, don't you cry; Hush, hush sweet

Char - lotte, I'll love you till I die. Oh,

I LOVE LUCY

Lyrics by HAROLD ADAMSON
Music by ELIOT DANIE[L]

I'M EASY

Words and Music by
KEITH CARRADINE

With feeling

It's not my way to love you just when no-one's look-ing. It's not my way to take your hand if I'm not sure. It's not my way to let you see what's go-ing on in-side of me; when it's a love you won't be need-ing, you're not free. Please stop

I'M HANS CHRISTIAN ANDERSEN

(From "HANS CHRISTIAN ANDERSEN")

By FRANK LOESSER

...hat blows high but that's not the end of that For

'round and 'round the world it goes and it lands here right be-

hind my-self, I pick it up, and I read the note, which is

mere-ly to re-mind my-self 3. I'M

D. S. al Fine

rit. _ _ _ _ _ _ _ _ *a tempo*

D. S. al Fine

I'M STILL HERE

Words and Music by
STEPHEN SONDHEIM

IF WE HOLD ON TOGETHER

Words and Music by JAMES HORNER
and WILL JENNINGS

Don't lose your way with each pass-ing day.
Souls in the wind must learn how to bend,

You've come so far, don't throw it a-way.
seek out a star, hold on to the end.

Live be-liev-ing
Val - ley, moun - tain,

IT MIGHT AS WELL BE SPRING

(From "STATE FAIR")

Lyrics by OSCAR HAMMERSTEIN II
Music by RICHARD RODGERS

THEME FROM "JAWS"

By JOHN WILLIAMS

THE JOHN DUNBAR THEME
(From "DANCES WITH WOLVES")

By JOHN BARRY

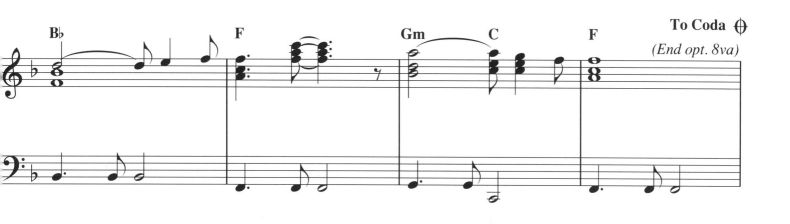

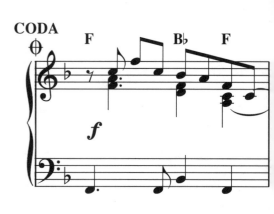

THE JETSONS (MAIN TITLE)
(From "THE JETSONS")

Words and Music by W. HANNA
and J. BARBERA

Meet   George   Jet - son!

KOKOMO
(From The Motion Picture "COCKTAIL")

Words and Music by MIKE LOVE, TERRY MELCHER,
JOHN PHILLIPS and SCOTT McKENZIE

Moderately bright

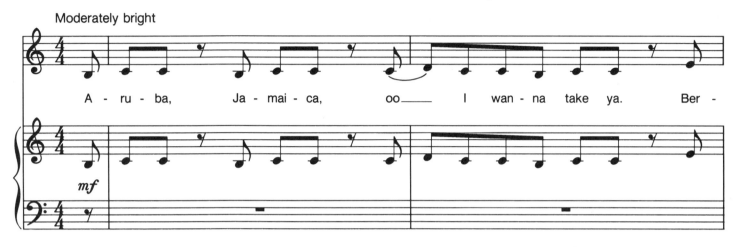

A-ru-ba, Ja-mai-ca, oo___ I wan-na take ya. Ber-

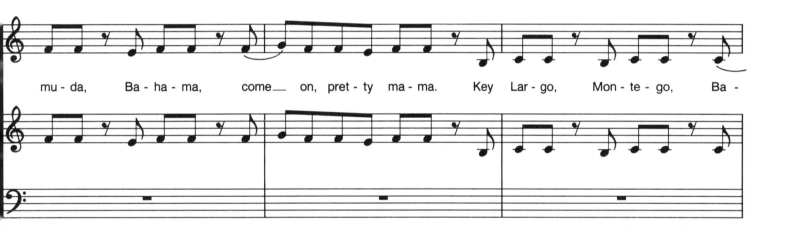

mu-da, Ba-ha-ma, come___ on, pret-ty ma-ma. Key Lar-go, Mon-te-go, Ba-

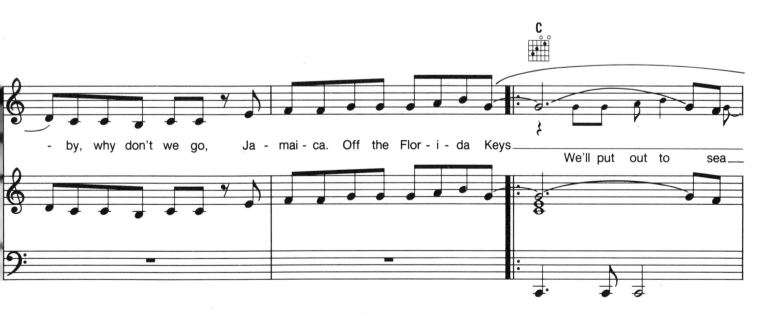

-by, why don't we go, Ja-mai-ca. Off the Flor-i-da Keys___ We'll put out to sea___

mu - da, Ba - ha - ma. Come___ on, pret - ty ma - ma. Key

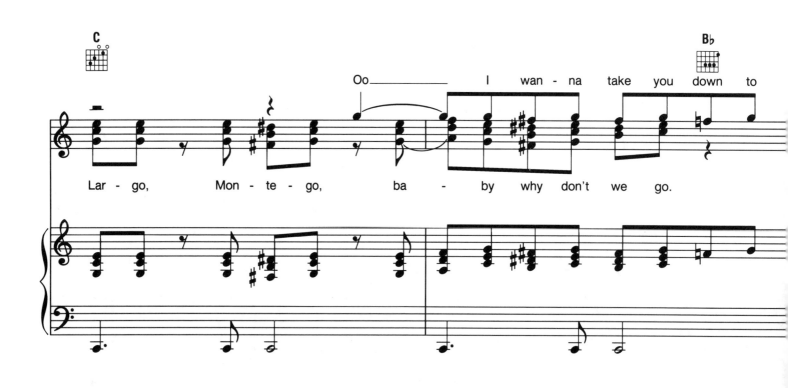

Oo___ I wan - na take you down to

Lar - go, Mon - te - go, ba - by why don't we go.

Ko - ko - mo.___ We'll get there fast___ and then we'll

KNOT'S LANDING

(Theme From The Lorimar Productions, Inc. Television Series)

Music by JERROLD IMME

THE LAST TIME I SAW PARIS

Words by OSCAR HAMMERSTEIN
Music by JEROME KERN

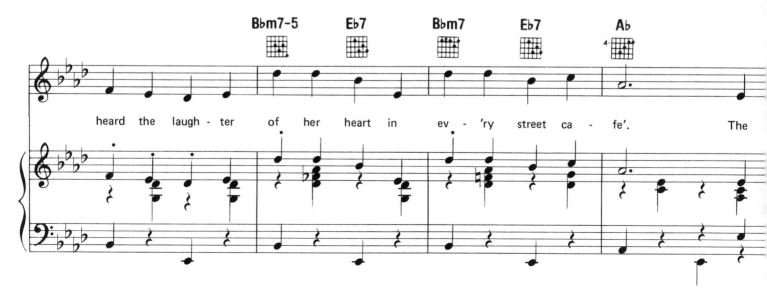

THE TOY PARADE
(Theme To "LEAVE IT TO BEAVER")

By D. KAHN,
M. LENARD and M. GREENE

Hey! Here they come with a rum - tee - tum they're

hav - ing a toy pa - rade, _____ a tin gi - raffe with a

pipe and drum is lead - ing the kew - pie bri - gade. _____ A

fee   fie   fid - dle   dee   dee   they're   up   to   the   din - ing   room

door._____   They   call   a   halt   for   a   choc - 'late   malt   or

cook - ies   and   lem - on - ade,_____   then   off   they   go   with   a

ho   ho   ho   right   back ___   to   their   toy   pa - rade._____

THE LITTLE HOUSE (On The Prairie)
(Theme from the TV Series)

Music by DAVID ROSE

MAJOR DAD
(Theme From TV Series)

By ROGER STEINMAN

MCA music publishing

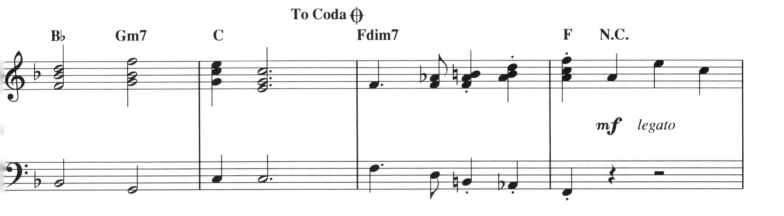

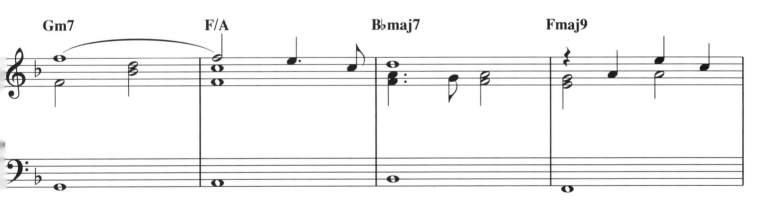

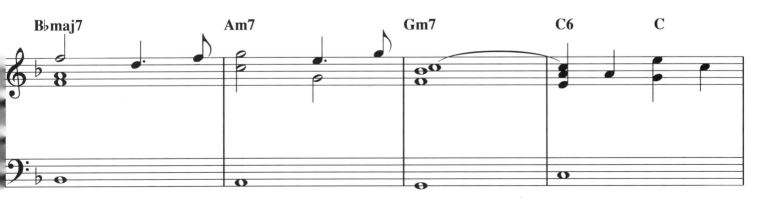

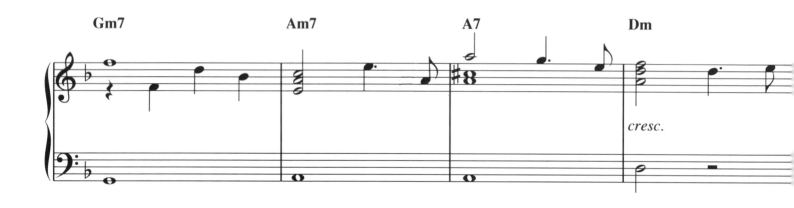

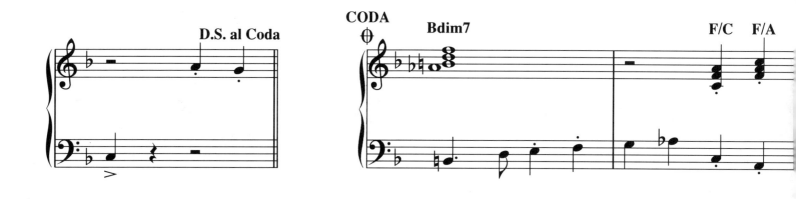

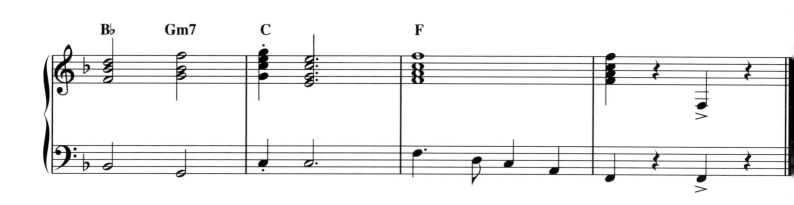

A MAN AND A WOMAN
(UN HOMME ET UNE FEMME)

Original Words by PIERRE BAROUH
English Words by JERRY KELLER
Music by FRANCIS LAI

THE MASTERPIECE
(The T.V. Theme from THE MASTERPIECE THEATER)

Moderately, with restraint

By J.J. MOURET and PAUL PARN

MCA music publishing

MIAMI VICE
(Theme from the Universal Television Series)

By JAN HAMMER

MCA music publishing

MICKEY MOUSE MARCH

(From Walt Disney's "THE MICKEY MOUSE CLUB")

Words and Music by
JIMMIE DODD

MIDNIGHT COWBOY

(From the Motion Picture "MIDNIGHT COWBOY")

Music by JOHN BARRY
Lyric by JACK GOLD

Moderately Slow

MR. ED

Words and Music by RAY EVANS
and JAY LIVINGSTON

MCA music publishing

MORE
(Theme From "MONDO CANE")

English Words by NORMAN NEWELL
Music by RIZ ORTOLANI and NINO OLIVIERO

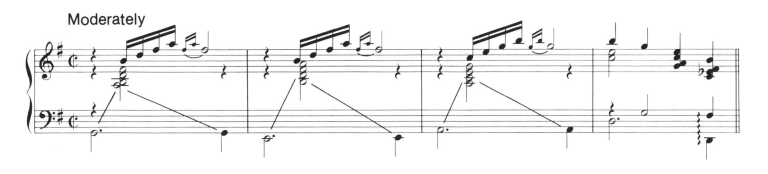

More than the great-est love the world has known;

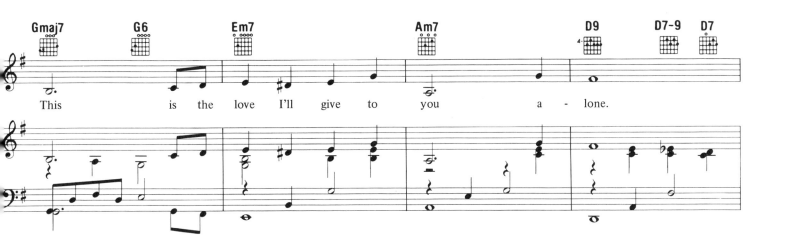

This is the love I'll give to you a - lone.

THE MUPPET SHOW THEME

By JIM HENSON
and SAM POTTLE

MYSTERY
(Theme From The PBS Television Series)

Music by
NORMAND ROGER

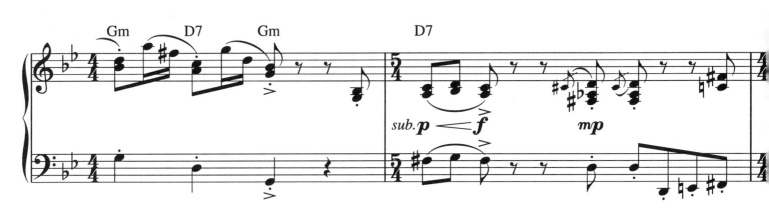

THE MUNSTER'S THEME

By JACK MARSHALL

Moderately Slow

MCA music publishing

MURDER, SHE WROTE

(Theme from the Universal Television Series "Murder, She Wrote")

Words and Music by
JOHN ADDISON

THE MUSIC OF GOODBYE
(Love Theme From "OUT OF AFRICA")

Words by ALAN and MARILYN BERGMAN
Music by JOHN BARRY

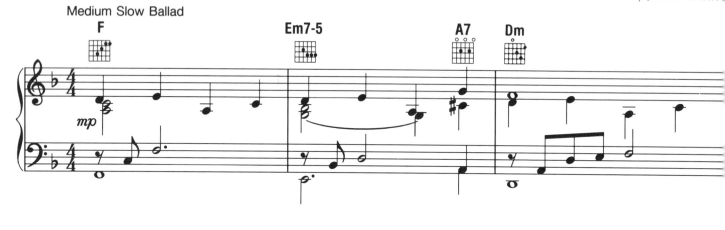

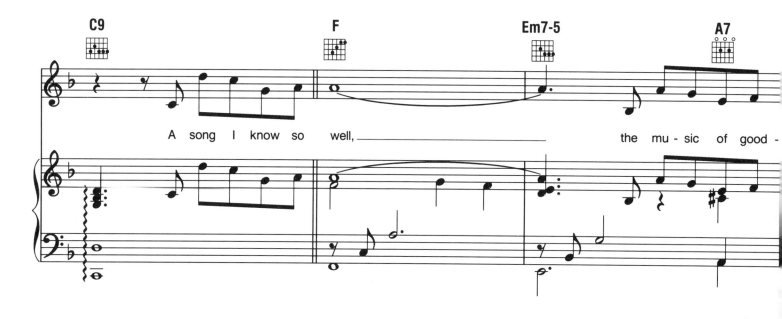

A song I know so well, _____ the mu-sic of good-

bye a-gain. _____ It's there each time we say "hel-lo." _____

MCA music publishing

NEVER ON SUNDAY
(From Jules Dassin's Motion Picture "NEVER ON SUNDAY")

Words by BILLY TOWN
Music by MANOS HADJIDAK

ON GOLDEN POND
(Main Theme)

Music by DAVE GRUS

Very freely

p very delicately, as though from far away

Andante rubato*

*Not fast and somewhat freely

Ped.

8va - - - - - - - - - - - - -

PENNIES FROM HEAVEN

Words by JOHN BURKE
Music by ARTHUR JOHNSTON

PERRY MASON THEME

Words and Music by
FRED STEINER

QUE SERA, SERA
(WHATEVER WILL BE, WILL BE)

Words and Music by JAY LIVINGSTON
and RAY EVANS

THE ROCKFORD FILES

(Theme From the Universal Television Series "THE ROCKFORD FILES")

Words and Music by MIKE POST
and PETE CARPENTER

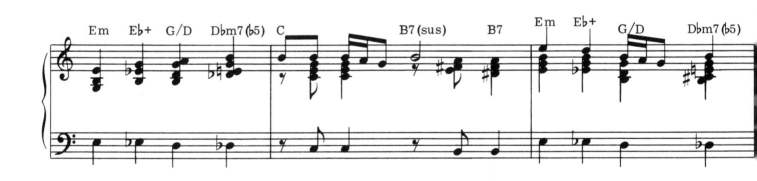

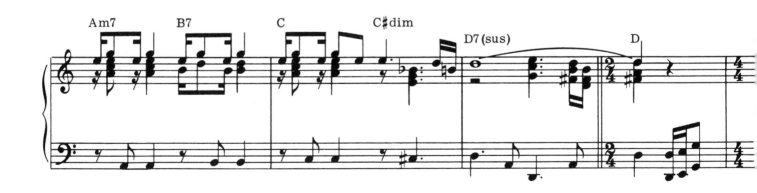

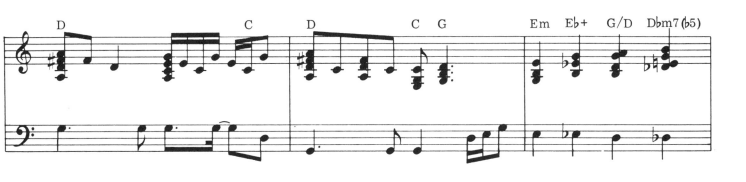

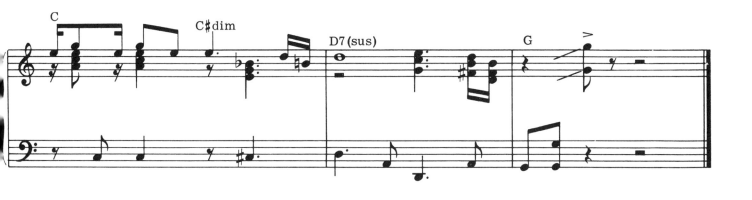

ROCKY & BULLWINKLE

By FRANK COMSTOCK

THE RAINBOW CONNECTION

By PAUL WILLIAMS and
KENNETH L. ASCHER

SOMEWHERE OUT THERE
(From "An American Tail")

By JAMES HORNER, BARRY MANN
and CYNTHIA WEIL

MCA music publishing

SECRET AGENT MAN

Bright Rock

Words and Music by P. F. SLOA
and STEVE BAR

1. There's a man who leads a life of dan-
ware of pret-ty fac-es that you find.
3. instrumental
4. Swing-ing on the Riv-i-er a one

-ger.
day.
And then lay-in' in a Bom
To ev-'ry-one he meets.
A pret-ty face can hide

MCA music publishing

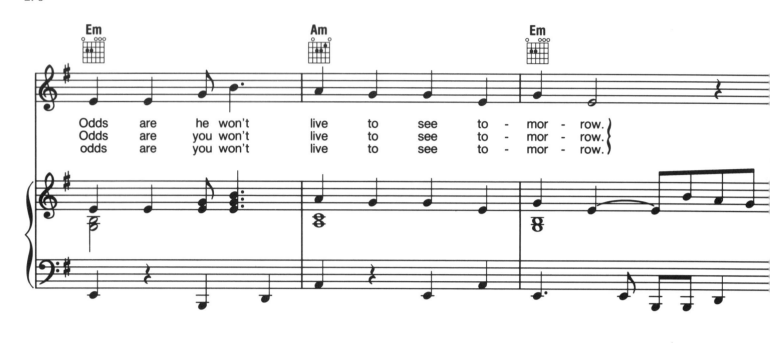

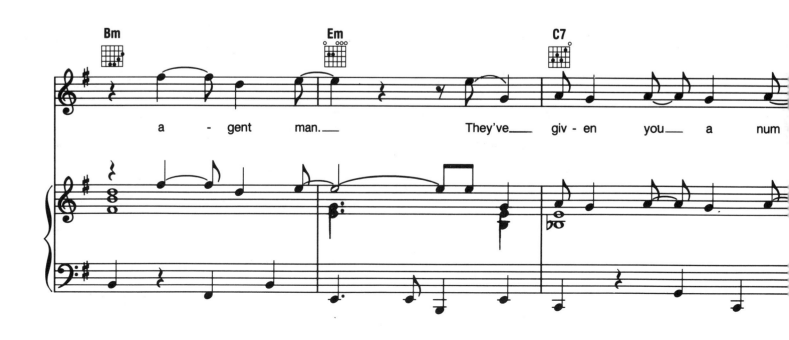

SEPARATE LIVES
(LOVE THEME FROM "WHITE NIGHTS")

Words and Music by
STEPHEN BISHOP

77 SUNSET STRIP

By MACK DAVID
and JERRY LIVINGSTON

SOONER OR LATER
(I ALWAYS GET MY MAN)

(From The film DICK TRACY)

Words and Music
STEPHEN SONDHE

THERE WILL NEVER BE ANOTHER YOU

(From "ICELAND")

Music by HARRY WARREN
Lyric by MACK GORDON

Lyrics:
This is our last dance to-geth-er, to-night soon will be long a-go. And in our mo-ment of part-ing, this is all I

THIRTYSOMETHING
(Main Title Theme)

By W.G. SNUFFY WALDEN
and STEWART LEVIN

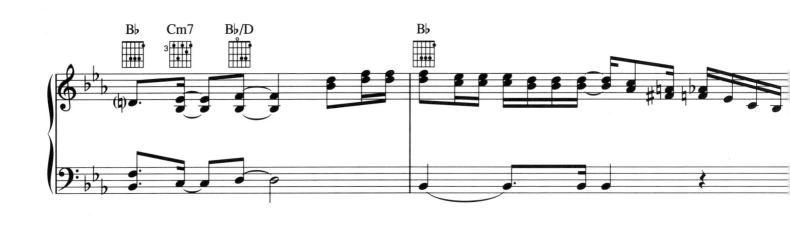

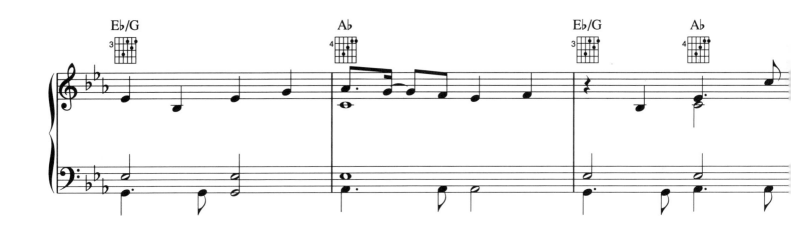

THIS IS IT
(Theme From "The Bugs Bunny Show")

Words and Music by MACK DAVID
and JERRY LIVINGSTON

TWILIGHT ZONE

Words and Music
MAURIUS CONSTA

THREE COINS IN THE FOUNTAIN

(From "THREE COINS IN THE FOUNTAIN")

Words by SAMMY CAH
Music by JULE STYN

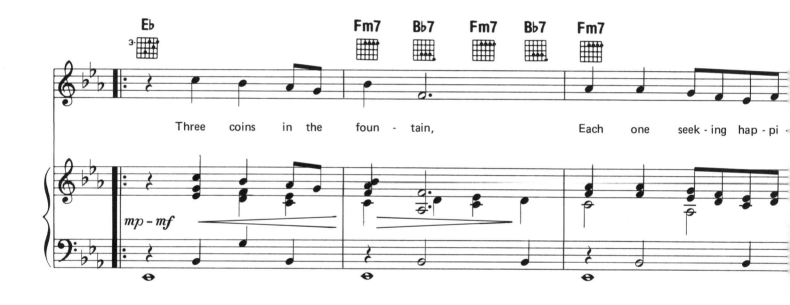

Three coins in the foun - tain, Each one seek-ing hap-pi

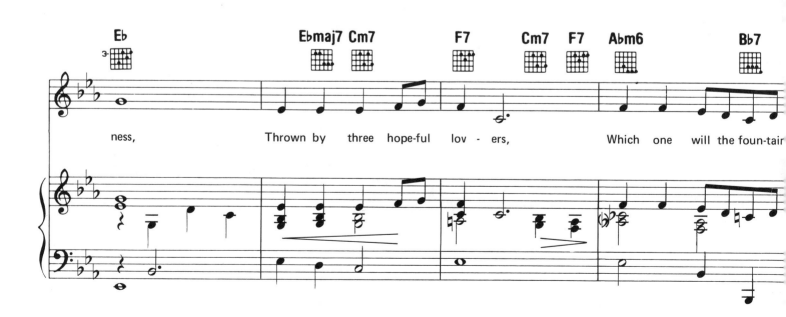

ness, Thrown by three hope-ful lov - ers, Which one will the foun-tair

313

THEME FROM "THE UNTOUCHABLES"

By NELSON RIDDLE

UNCHAINED MELODY
(From "UNCHAINED")

Lyric by HY ZARET
Music by ALEX NORTH

UNDER THE SEA
(From Walt Disney's "THE LITTLE MERMAID")

Lyrics by HOWARD ASHMAN
Music by ALAN MENKEN

The sea - weed is al - ways green - er
Down here __ all the fish is hap - py

in some - bod - y else - 's lake.
as off __ through the waves dey roll.

You dream __ a - bout
The fish __ on the

go - ing up there.
land ain't hap - py.

But that __ is a big mis - take.
They sad __ 'cause they in the bowl.

Un - der the sea.   Un - der the

sea.   When __ the sar - dine be - gin __ the be -

330

VICTORY AT SEA

By RICHARD RODGERS

Moderate tempo, tempestuous

WHAT A WONDERFUL WORLD
(Featured in the Motion Picture "GOOD MORNING VIETNAM")

Words and Music by GEORGE DAVID WEI
and BOB THIE

WON'T YOU BE MY NEIGHBOR?

(From "MR. ROGERS NEIGHBORHOOD")

Words and Music
FRED ROG...

YELLOW SUBMARINE

Words and Music
JOHN LENNON and PAUL McCARTNEY

March tempo

ZIP-A-DEE-DOO-DAH
(From Walt Disney's "SONG OF THE SOUTH")

Words by RAY GILBERT
Music by ALLIE WRUBEL

THE WAY YOU LOOK TONIGHT

Words by DOROTHY FIEL[
Music by JEROME KE[

Some day when I'm aw-f'ly low, When the world is
love - ly, With your smile so warm, And your cheek so

cold, I will feel a glow just think-ing of you
soft, There is noth-ing for me but to love you,

And the way you look to - night.
Just the way you look to - night. Oh, but you're

26 CONTEMPORARY HITS

An assortment of today's favorite hits, including: Achy Breaky Heart • Baby Baby • Beauty And The Beast • Make It Happen • Save The ~~st~~ For Last • Tears In Heaven • This Used ~~Be~~ My Playground • Where Does My ~~art~~ Beat Now • and many more.
~~311599~~ $12.95

Contemporary CLASSICS

LIGHT HITS FROM YESTERDAY & TODAY!
ARRANGED FOR PIANO, VOICE & GUITAR

EASY LISTENING STANDARDS

75 classic and contemporary favorites, including: Chances Are • Edelweiss • Endless Love • A Foggy Day • Just The Way You Are • Misty • My Way • People • Somewhere Out There • Strangers In The Night • and many more.
00311504 $14.95

60 CONTEMPORARY CLASSICS

60 of the best-loved contemporary pop songs, including: Careless Whisper • Could I Have This Dance • Holding Back The Years • Just The Way You Are • Longer • Memory • Sara • Stand By Me • These Dreams • What's Love Got To Do With It • You Give Good Love • and more.
00361078 $16.95

THE NEW GRAMMY AWARDS SONG OF THE YEAR SONGBOOK

An updated edition that features every song named Grammy Awards "Song of the Year" from 1958-1988. 28 songs, featuring: Volare • Moon River • The Shadow Of Your Smile • Up, Up And Away • Bridge Over Troubled Water • You've Got A Friend • Killing Me Softly With His Song • The Way We Were • You Light Up My Life • Evergreen • Sailing • Bette Davis Eyes • We Are The World • That's What Friends Are For • Somewhere Out There • Don't Worry, Be Happy.
00359932 $12.95

66 CONTEMPORARY STANDARDS

66 contemporary classics, including: All Around The World • Black Velvet • Candle In The Wind • Careless Whisper • Every Breath You Take • Every Rose Has Its Thorn • Here And Now • Hold On • How Am I Supposed To Live Without You • I Wanna Be Rich • Imagine • Kokomo • Memory • Red, Red Wine • Sacrifice • Time After Time • We Didn't Start The Fire • What's Love Got To Do With • You Needed Me • and more.
~~490501~~ $16.95

NEW AGE PIANO SAMPLER

11 new age selections by Yanni, John Jarvis, Suzanne Ciani, Jim Chappell and Eddie Jobson. Includes biographies and photos of each featured artist. Pieces include: Velocity Of Love • After The Sunrise • Homecoming • and more.
00360690 $10.95

THE ADULT CONTEMPORARY SONGBOOK

48 of today's best light hits, including: Candle In The Wind • Don't Know Much • Every Breath You Take • How Can We Be Lovers • Love Takes Time • Sacrifice • Somewhere Out There • Vision Of Love • and many more.
00311529 $15.95

RHYTHM & BLUES BALLADS

34 wonderful ballads by some of the best R&B artists–Earth, Wind & Fire, Gregory Abbott, Luther Vandross, Angela Bofill, and Gladys Knight & The Pips. Songs include: Careless Whisper • Earth Angel • Just Once • Sara Smile • Sexual Healing • Shake You Down • and more.
00360870 $12.95

CONTEMPORARY BALLADS

58 favorite ballads, including: Can't Smile Without You • Careless Whisper • Endless Love • Green Green Grass Of Home • Just The Way You Are • Let It Be • Longer • Love On The Rocks • My Way • Same Old Lang Syne • Sometimes When We Touch • Time After Time • Yesterday • You Needed Me • more.
00359492 $16.95

SOFT ROCK-REVISED

40 romantic mellow hits, including: And So It Goes • Beauty And The Beast • Don't Know Much • Save The Best For Last • Tears In Heaven • Vision Of Love • Your Song • and more.
00311596 $14.95

CONTEMPORARY LOVE & WEDDING SONGS

26 songs of romance, including: Can't Help Falling In Love • Could I Have This Dance • Endless Love • I.O.U. • Just The Way You Are • Longer • Somewhere Out There • Sunrise, Sunset • You Needed Me • Your Song.
00359498 $10.95

TIMELESS HITS

32 pop standards, including: Copacabana • Could I Have This Dance • Fire And Rain • Green Green Grass Of Home • I.O.U. • Longer • Piano Man • Stand By Me • We're In This Love Together • What A Wonderful World • You Are My Lady.
00490095 $12.95

For more information, see your local music dealer, or write to:

Hal Leonard Publishing Corporation

P.O. Box 13819 Milwaukee, Wisconsin 53213

Prices, contents, and availability subject to change without notice.

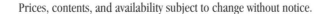